W0006692

This book is due for return on or before the last date shown below.

sswell Ltd., London, N21   Cat. No. 1208

DG 02242/71

A MEMBER OF THE HODDER HEADLINE GROUP

**Acknowledgements**
*Cover: Dave Smith*
*Illustrations: Mike Bell*

Orders; please contact Bookpoint Ltd, 39 Milton Park, Abingdon, Oxon OX14
4TD. Telephone: (44) 01235 400414, Fax: (44) 01235 400454. Lines are open
from 9.00–6.00, Monday to Saturday, with a 24 hour message answering service.
Email address: orders@bookpoint.co.uk

*British Library Cataloguing in Publication Data*
A catalogue record for this title is available from the British Library

ISBN  0 340 77514 9

First published  2000
Impression number  10 9 8 7 6 5 4 3 2 1
Year                          2005 2004 2003 2002 2001 2000

Copyright © 2000  Brandon Robshaw

Typeset by GreenGate Publishing Services, Tonbridge, Kent.
Printed in Great Britain for Hodder and Stoughton Educational, a division of
Hodder Headline Plc, 338 Euston Road, London NW1 3BH, by Atheneum
Press, Gateshead, Tyne & Wear

# Jason and the Golden Fleece

## Contents

## How to pronounce the names    Who's who

**Iolcus** – Yol-cus                      Country where Peleas ruled.

**Peleas** – Pee-lee-as                   King of Iolcus.

**Hera** – Hee-ra                         Queen of the gods.

**Colchis** – Col-kiss                    Home of the Golden Fleece.

**Argonauts** – Ar-go-norts               Band of heroes who travel with Jason.

**Hercules** – Her-kew-leez               Mighty warrior (an Argonaut).

**Zetes** – Zee-teez  }
**Calais** – Ca-lay   }                   Men with wings (both Argonauts) who chased away the Harpies.

**Poeas** – Pee-as                        An archer (and Argonaut) who helps Jason win against the Brass Giant.

**Orpheus** – Or-fee-us                   A gifted musician (and Argonaut).

**Phineus** – Fin-ee-us                   King cursed by the Harpies.

**Harpies** – Har-peez                    Creatures with the body of a woman and the wings and claws of a bird.

**Aeetes** – Eye-ee-teez                  Fierce King of Colchis who sets Jason two difficult tasks.

**Medea** – Med-ear                       Daughter of King Aeetes who agrees to help Jason if he marries her. (A witch.)

**Hesperides** – Hes-per-i-deez           A special place with a garden of golden apples.

**Circe** – Sir-see                       Medea's aunt (and a witch).

**Sirens** – Si-renz                      Winged creatures who trick sailors by singing to them and then kill them.

# 1

# Jason's Early Years

Jason was Prince of Iolcus.
One day, he would be King.
However, when Jason was still a child
his Uncle Peleas took over the throne.
He would have killed Jason but
luckily friends took Jason away in time.
To keep him safe, they took him to a centaur –
a creature with a man's head
and a horse's body.

So Jason was brought up in the centaur's cave,
in the mountains.
Many years went by.
Jason grew tall and strong.
When he was a young man,
he left the centaur's cave in the mountains.
He went to Iolcus to face his Uncle Peleas.

Peleas was still King of Iolcus –
but he was a worried man.
He had been told that
a man with one sandal
would cause his death.
Every time a stranger came to Iolcus,
Peleas was afraid.
So far, the man with one sandal
had not arrived.

On his way to Iolcus,
Jason came to a river.
An old woman was sitting by it.
'I am too weak to cross,' she said.
'Can you help me?'

3

'Of course,' said Jason and
he picked the old woman up.
As he carried her across,
one of his sandals was lost in the river.

He put her down on the other side –
then stared in amazement.
The old woman had changed
into a beautiful goddess
'Don't be afraid, Jason,' she said.
'I am the goddess Hera.
Go on to Iolcus.
You will become
one of the most famous heroes in Greece.'
Then she disappeared.
Thoughtfully, Jason went on his way.

# 2

# The Quest

That evening, Jason arrived at Iolcus.
King Peleas was in the middle of a feast.
Some heavy drinking was going on
and the hall was crowded and noisy.
When Jason walked in the hall
there was a sudden hush.
Everyone stared.
It was the man with one sandal!

King Peleas found his voice.
'Who are you?'

'I am Jason,' said the young man.
'Your nephew.'

'Really?' said King Peleas.
His heart sank – but he didn't show it.
'It's good to see you
after all these years,' he lied.
'Listen, Jason, I've got something to ask you.
If you'd been told someone
would cause your death,
how would you get rid of him?'

'I'd send him to get the Golden Fleece,'
said Jason, without thinking.

'Good!' said Peleas, clapping his hands.
'I was told that a man with one sandal
would cause my death – and here you are.
So go and get me the Golden Fleece.'

The Golden Fleece was the fleece
of a magic ram, made of pure gold.
It hung from a tree
in the far-off country of Colchis.
It was guarded by a huge dragon.
Jason couldn't have thought of
a more dangerous task.

Jason was no coward.
He looked King Peleas in the eye.
'Right,' he said.
'I'll be back.'

# 3

# The Argo

The first thing Jason did
was to have a ship built.
A shipbuilder called Argus made it for him.
Jason called the ship the *Argo*.

Next, Jason sent messengers all over Greece.
He asked anyone who wanted an adventure
to join him.
Fifty brave, strong heroes came
from all over Greece.
They were known as 'the Argonauts'.

Among them was the mighty Hercules.
There were Zetes and Calais,
who had wings and could fly.
There was the archer, Poeas.
There was also Orpheus, a musician.
He could play and sing so beautifully
that even wild animals stopped to listen.

The *Argo* set sail.
One of their first landings
was in the country of King Phineus.
Phineus made them welcome
and gave them a feast.
'Can you tell us how to get to Colchis?'
asked Jason.

'I'll help you – if you free me
from the Harpies!' said Phineus.

'Harpies?' asked Jason.
'What are they?'

'Here they come now!' said Phineus.
He pointed at the sky.
Two creatures flew down.
They had the head and body of a woman
but the wings and claws of a bird.
They snatched all the food off the table.
Then they flew away.

Zetes and Calais, the winged heroes,
drew their swords and flew after the Harpies.
They were never seen again.
Neither were the Harpies.
They must all have been killed in the fight.

King Phineus gave Jason advice
on how to get to Colchis.
Jason thanked him and
carried on with his journey.

# 4

# The Clashing
# Rocks

Rising out of the sea ahead,
they saw the Clashing Rocks.
These were two great rocks
that clashed together and
smashed any ship that tried to get through.

King Phineus had warned them about this
and Jason knew what to do.

He let loose a bird.
The bird flew towards the Clashing Rocks.
As it passed through, they clashed together.
They just missed the bird.
As the rocks drew apart,
Jason headed straight for the gap.
All the heroes pulled at the oars
as hard as they could.
They got through just in time.
The rocks clashed again,
just scraping the back of the *Argo*.

After that, it was plain sailing.
They sailed over the sea
and up the river that led to Colchis.

Colchis was ruled by King Aeetes.
Aeetes was no soft touch.
He was a fierce, warlike King.
'What do you want?' he roared at Jason.
'We have come to seek the Golden Fleece,'
Jason replied.

Aeetes didn't see why
he should give up the Golden Fleece.
'Before I let you try for the Fleece,'
he said, 'I must set you a little task.
I've got a team of magic bulls.
Their feet are made of brass
and they breathe fire.
I want you to tie them to a plough
and plough my field with them.
You must then plant some dragons' teeth.
Can you do that?'

'I'll try,' said Jason.
He didn't like the sound of this.

King Aeetes had a daughter, Medea.
She was very beautiful –
and she was a witch.

As soon as she saw Jason,
she wanted him.
She took him to one side.
'I'll help you get the Fleece,'
she said, 'if you marry me
and take me back to Greece.
Is it a deal?'

Jason looked at the beautiful witch.
'It's a deal,' he said.

# 5

# Dragons Teeth

The next day,
King Aeetes took Jason out to the field.
Jason looked at the huge bulls.
They pawed the ground with their br..  feet
and breathed out flames.

The King handed Jason a helmet.
It was full of dragons' teeth.
'Plant these when you've ploughed the field.'
He laughed.
'*If* you plough the field!'

Jason walked up to the bulls.
They snorted and breathed fire on him
but the fire did not hurt him.
Medea had given Jason a magic ointment
to protect him from the flames.
Calmly, he tied the bulls to the plough.

When the field was ploughed,
Jason scattered the dragons' teeth.
At once, each tooth grew into a soldier.
They attacked Jason with their swords.
Medea had told Jason what to do.
He threw the helmet to the ground.
The soldiers began to fight over it
and killed each other.

Jason turned to King Aeetes.
'That's done, then.
Now, what about that Fleece?'

The King looked very angry.
'You can have the Fleece tomorrow,' he said.

That night, Medea woke Jason up.
'My father is planning to kill you,' she said.
'We must take the Fleece and escape.
Come with me – and bring Orpheus.'

Jason woke Orpheus up.
They followed Medea through the moonlight.

# 6

# The Dragon

The Fleece hung from the top
of a tall tree.
A huge dragon lay coiled
around the trunk.
This dragon never slept.
Its terrible eyes glared
at Jason, Medea and Orpheus.

'Quick, Orpheus!' said Medea.
'Sing the dragon to sleep!'
Orpheus began to sing.
He sang so sweetly
that the terrible dragon's eyes
closed in sleep.

'Now, Jason,' said Medea,
'I can keep the dragon asleep by my magic –
but only for a short time.
Climb up and get the Fleece –
and do it quickly!'

Jason climbed over the huge dragon,
hoping it wouldn't wake.
He climbed up to the top of the tree.
He grabbed the Golden Fleece
and climbed down quickly.

They ran from the garden.
'Get your men on board the *Argo*!' said Medea.
'We must leave at once.
I'll get my little brother –
I want him to come with us.'

They boarded the ship
and set sail before it was light.
They were not safe yet.
When the sun rose,
they saw King Aeetes's ships following them.

# 7

# Murder

Jason's men pulled hard at the oars.
But King Aeetes's ships
were bigger and faster than the *Argo*.
Soon, they'd catch up.

'My father will kill us all
if he catches us,' said Medea.
'There's only one thing to do.'

King Aeetes was close enough now
to see what she did next.
She took out a knife
and stabbed her little brother.
Then she cut him into pieces.
One by one, she threw the pieces into the sea.

In rage and grief,
King Aeetes begged the gods
to put a curse on the *Argo*.
Then, he stopped his ships
to fish for the pieces of his son.
He wanted to be able to bury him.

The *Argo* sailed on.
'There!' said Medea.
'Made it!'

Jason and the heroes said nothing.
They were too shocked to speak.
Jason stared at Medea.
What sort of woman had he agreed to marry?

# 8

# Lost at Sea

Soon the curse of King Aeetes began to work.
The gods caused a great storm to blow up,
to punish Medea's crime.
The sky grew dark.
Rain battered the *Argo*.
The wind blew it off course.

The wind drove them up a river.
The river became a stream.
The heroes had to get out
and carry the *Argo* over land.
Half dead with tiredness,
they reached another river.
This river carried them
to a sea of ice and fog.
Cold, tired and hungry,
they sailed for months.

At long last they reached warmer seas.
'I know where we are' said Hercules.
'We are near the Garden of the Hesperides.
This is where I took the Golden Apples from,
fifteen years ago.'

They landed and Hercules showed them the tree
where the Golden Apples grew.

Near it, they saw the snake
that Hercules had killed fifteen years earlier.
To their amazement,
its tail was still twitching.

They sailed on.
They came to the island
where Circe the witch lived.
Circe was Medea's aunt.
By her magic powers,
she lifted the curse on the *Argo*.
At last, the heroes could sail home.

However, Jason's adventures
were not over yet.

# 9

# The Giant of Brass

They passed the island of the Sirens.
The Sirens were women with claws and wings.
They sang so sweetly
that any sailor who heard them
would jump ship and swim to them.
Then the Sirens would tear him to pieces.

Jason asked Orpheus to play his lyre.
Orpheus played and sang so beautifully
that the heroes listened to him instead.
This way the heroes got safely past the Sirens.

They sailed past the island of Crete.
On this island was a giant man made of brass.
He would run around the island,
throwing great rocks at passing ships.
The King of Crete had escaped him
and joined Jason's heroes.
'Help me get rid of this monster,' he begged.

'I'll sort him out,' said Medea.
She called to the man of brass.
'If you let me land with a friend,
I can make you King of the World!' she said.

The giant listened to Medea.
He liked the offer.
He let Medea land and Poeas came with her.
Poeas was small and did not look dangerous
but he was a deadly shot with a bow and arrow.

Medea made a magic brew for the giant.
'Drink this,' she said.
'It will make you King of the World.'
The giant drank.
The magic brew made him drunk.
He staggered around the island.

The giant had one weakness.
In his heel was a stopper.
If the stopper was pulled out,
his life-blood would flow away.
Poeas took aim with his bow and shot.
The arrow hit the giant's heel
and knocked the stopper out.
The blood began to flow.
The giant fell to the ground.
Soon he was a lifeless, brass statue.

The heroes landed on Crete
and there was a great feast.

Then Jason and Medea returned to Iolcus
with the Golden Fleece.

# 10

# Medea's Trick

Jason and Medea settled in Iolcus.
They had two children.
King Peleas agreed that Jason
should be King after his death.

Medea didn't want to wait
for Peleas to die.
She wanted to be Queen right away.
So she thought of a trick.

She said to Peleas's daughters,
'Your father is getting old.
Wouldn't you like to make him young again?'

'Yes, of course,' said the daughters.

'I know a spell for that,'
said Medea. 'Watch.'
She took an old ram and killed it.
She cut it into pieces and threw it in a pot.
At once, a young lamb jumped out.
'See?' said Medea.
'If you do that to your father,
he'll be young again.'

So the daughters killed their father.
They cut him into pieces
and put him in Medea's pot.

Their father did not come back to life.
He stayed in pieces.
Medea had not told his daughters
the magic spell.

Peleas was out of the way now –
but Medea did not become Queen.
The people of Iolcus
were so angry at what Medea had done,
they chased her and Jason from the land.

Jason and Medea wandered
until they came to Corinth.
There, they settled again.
It was in Corinth that …

That's another story.